D0443530

ANGRY BIRDS™
STAR WARS™

YODA BIRD'S HEROES

Written by Ruth Amos

DK

LONDON, NEW YORK, MUNICH,
MELBOURNE and DELHI

Editorial Assistant Ruth Amos
Senior Editor Elizabeth Dowsett
Senior Designer Lynne Moulding
Jacket Designer Lynne Moulding
Pre-production Producer Marc Staples
Producer Charlotte Oliver
Managing Editor Laura Gilbert
Design Manager Maxine Pedliham
Art Director Ron Stobbart
Publishing Director Simon Beecroft

Reading Consultant Maureen Fernandes

Lucasfilm
Executive Editor J. W. Rinzler
Art Director Troy Alders
Keeper of the Holocron Leland Chee
Director of Publishing Carol Roeder

Rovio
Approvals Editor Nita Ukkonen
Senior Graphic Designer Jan Schulte-Tigges
Content Manager Laura Nevanlinna
Vice President of Book Publishing Sanna Lukander

First published in Great Britain in 2013 by
Dorling Kindersley Limited
80 Strand, London WC2R 0RL

10 9 8 7 6 5 4 3 2 1
001–193696–March/13

A CIP catalogue record for this book
is available from the British Library.

ISBN: 978-1-40933-310-4

Colour reproduction by Altaimage, UK
Printed and bound in Slovakia by TBB, a.s.

Discover more at
www.dk.com
www.starwars.com

Contents

ANGRY BIRDS™
STAR WARS™

YODA BIRD'S
HEROES

Written by Ruth Amos

The Bird Rebels

The Bird Rebels are
fighting to save the galaxy!

They must defend the galaxy
from the naughty pigs.

Chuck
"Ham" Solo

Princess
Stella
Organa

galaxy

Red
Skywalker

Yoda Bird

Yoda Bird is leading his flock
to protect the Bird Republic.

Unlike the pigs, the birds want
to live in peace and harmony.

Terebacca

Obi-Wan Kaboomi

R2-EGG2

C-3PYOLK

The villains

Look out! These are the naughty pigs from the Pig Empire.

The porky pigs want to eat all the sweets and junk food in the galaxy.

Pig Pilot

Pigtrooper

Emperor
Piglatine

Emperor Piglatine is the evil leader of the Pig Empire.

He orders the pigs to attack Yoda Bird and his flock.

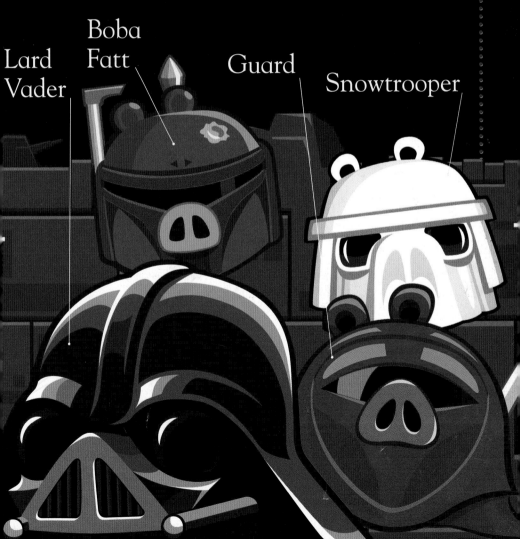

Lard Vader

Boba Fatt

Guard

Snowtrooper

Yoda Bird

This is Yoda Bird.

He is a very wise and old Jedi.

Brave Yoda protects
the birds with his
lightsaber weapon.

Wrinkly
forehead

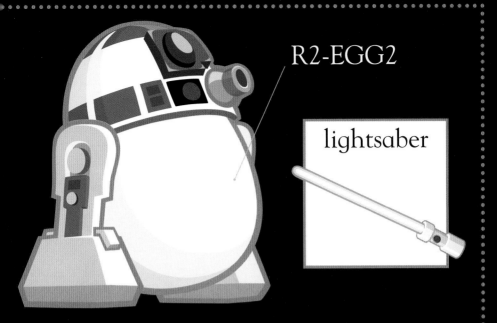

R2-EGG2

lightsaber

Yoda Bird has a secret.
He is the only bird who
knows where The Egg is!

The Egg has the power
to rule the galaxy.

Yoda disguised The Egg as
the robot bird R2-EGG2.

Floppy
hair

Red Skywalker

Red Skywalker is learning
how to be a Jedi warrior.
He thinks that he knows
everything already!

Red is determined to find
The Egg before the naughty
pigs get their trotters on it!

Red is very clumsy.
He is always dropping his
lightsaber on the floor and
walking into things!

Jedi
robes

Obi-Wan Kaboomi

Obi-Wan Kaboomi is Red
Skywalker's powerful Jedi Master.

Obi-Wan is very pleased
with his strong Jedi powers.

Brown
cloak

Obi-Wan knows how to do lots of different tricks with his blue lightsaber.

Like his leader Yoda, Obi-Wan uses his lightsaber in battle to defend the galaxy.

Glowing
lightsaber

Training together

Obi-Wan and Red have lots
of Jedi training classes.

Obi-Wan instructs Red on
proper Jedi behaviour.

Obi-Wan talks about his
marvellous Jedi powers.
Sometimes Red does not listen!

Obi-Wan gets annoyed.
Red thinks that his teacher's
grumpy face is really funny!

Tuft of
feathers

Plaited bun

Princess Stella

This is her royal highness,
Princess Stella Organa.

Stella is one of the
most important
Bird Republic leaders.
She works very hard.

squawking

Red and Stella are secretly very jealous of each other's hair.

They have big, squawking arguments over who has the best hairdo.

Stella does not tell Red she wants to swap hair with him!

Chuck "Ham" Solo

This yellow fellow
is called Ham.
He is a great shot
with his blaster.

blaster

He joined the Bird Rebels
to help them fight
for the Bird Republic.

Ham smuggles junk food around the galaxy in his *Mighty Falcon* starship.

He also uses it to rescue the birds when they are in trouble.

Mighty Falcon

Birds of a feather

Stella and Ham are really good friends.

Sometimes they coo at each other like a pair of lovebirds.

But sometimes Princess Stella gets very cross if Ham disagrees with her!

Watch out, Ham!

Bandolier belt

Terebacca

Terebacca is Ham's biggest, fluffiest friend.

His huge feathers protect him from the cold.

Terebacca grunts and moans
instead of talking.
Ham can still understand him.

Terebacca and Ham are always
laughing and joking about
their silly adventures.

Thick
feathers

C-3PYOLK

C-3PYOLK is a droid bird,
with a shiny golden body.

C-3PYOLK is a robot of peace,
who squawks all day long
about staying out of trouble.

C-3PYOLK wants
to stop the battles
between the birds
and the pigs.

droid

This is because fighting
makes C-3PYOLK nervous!

Big,
clever
eyes

R2-EGG2

R2-EGG2 does not know he is the disguise for The Egg!

The Egg is very powerful because it contains the Force.

Camera eye

The Force is a power
that can rule the galaxy.

R2-EGG2 is a droid bird,
like his friend, C-3PYOLK.

R2-EGG2 always tries to look
after C-3PYOLK.

Red
Skywalker
pilot

Flyboys

Red Skywalker and the
rest of his squadron
are amazing pilots!

They zoom along
at top speed in their
X-wing Birdfighters.

Sometimes they fly so fast
that it makes them dizzy.

R2-EGG2 sits in the back of
Red's Birdfighter to help him fly
and save the galaxy.

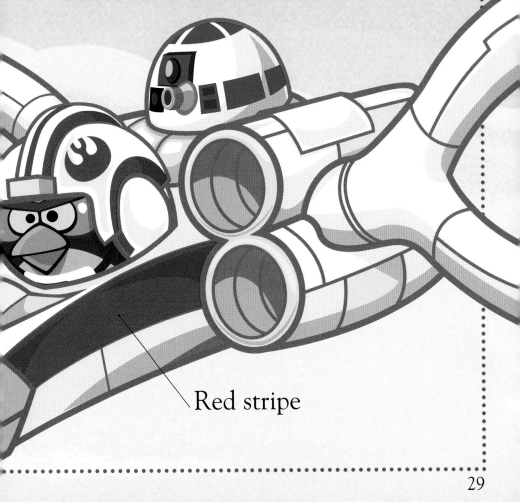

Red stripe

TIE fighter

Space battle

These sinister swine are
attacking the Bird Rebels.

The pigs launch their TIE fighter
aircraft through the air.

Yoda leads
his flock
into battle.
The birds fight back bravely.

The Bird Rebel heroes have
saved the galaxy – this time!

Glossary

Blaster
A weapon that shoots out laser blasts.

Droid
A robot.

Galaxy
A group of stars and planets.

Lightsaber
A sword-like weapon that has a beam made of pure energy.

Squawking
A harsh, shrieking noise that birds make.

Index